A Note to Parents and Teachers

SAINSBURY'S READING SCHEME is a compelling new programme for beginning readers, designed in conjunction with leading literacy experts, including Dr Linda Gambrell, President of the National Reading Conference and past board member of the International Reading Association.

Beautiful illustrations and superb full-colour photographs combine with engaging, easy-to-read stories to offer a fresh approach to each subject in the series. Each book in the SAINSBURY'S READING SCHEME programme is guaranteed to capture a child's interest while developing his or her reading skills, general knowledge and love of reading.

The five levels of the programme are aimed at different reading abilities, enabling you to choose the books that are exactly right for your child:

Yellow Level – Learning to read
Green Level – Beginning to read
Gold Level – Beginning to read alone
Ruby Level – Reading alone
Sapphire Level – Proficient readers

The "normal" age at which a child begins to read can be anywhere from three to eight years old, so these levels are only a general guideline.

No matter which level you select, you can be sure that you are helping your child learn to read, wthen read to learn!

LONDON, NEW YORK, MUNICH,
MELBOURNE AND DELHI

Editor Dawn Sirett
Art Editor Jane Horne
Senior Editor Ros Walford
Senior Art Editor Diane Thistlethwaite
US Editor Regina Kahney
Production Editor Kavita Varma
Production Controller Charlotte Oliver
Picture Researcher Cynthia Frazer
Jacket Designer David McDonald

Natural History Consultant
Theresa Greenaway

Reading Consultant
Linda Gambrell, Ph.D.

This edition published in 2011
First published in Great Britain 2000 by
Dorling Kindersley Limited
80 Strand, London WC2R 0RL
Penguin Group (UK)

A CIP record for this book is available from the British Library

ISBN 978-1-4053-7561-0

Colour reproduction by Colourscan, Singapore
Printed and bound in China by L Rex Printing Co., Ltd.

The publisher would like to thank the following for their kind
permission to reproduce their photographs:
c=centre; b=below; l=left; r=right t=top;

Heather Angel: 11tr, 13tr, 15br; **Ardea London Ltd:** Ian Beames 1br,
9br, 17 inset, 17br, 19tr, 32cra, R.J.C. Blewitt 23t, Rosie Bomford 6–7t,
M. Watson 4–5b, 21br; **Bruce Coleman Collection Ltd:** Antonio
Manzanares 14 inset, 32tr, William S. Paton 16–17b, 20–21b, Hans
Reinhard 3b, 25 br, Jens Rydell 14–15t, Kim Taylor 7b, 30–31, Colin
Varndell 24–25t; **Ecoscene:** R. Redfern 29t; **NHPA:** John Shaw 12–13b;
Oxford Scientific Films: G.I. Bernard 17t, Scott Camazine 30tl, tr, cra,
br, Philippe Henry 12cl, 32bl, Michael Leach 28b, T.C. Nature 10–11b,
K.G. Vock/Okapia 22b; **Papilio Photographic:** 8–9t; **Planet Earth
Pictures:** Richard Coomber 22cra, 32crb; **Telegraph Colour Library:** 5c,
32tl, Steve Bloom 26t, Phillip Chapman 26–27b.

All other images © Dorling Kindersley
For further information see: www.dkimages.com

Discover more at
www.dk.com

Sainsbury's
Reading Scheme

Green Level
Learning to read

Animals that Hibernate

Written by Karen Wallace

A fluffy-tailed dormouse
stops by a meadow.

Cold rain is falling.
Soon snow will be coming.

The dormouse is looking
for somewhere to sleep.
She needs a bed for the winter.

meadow

A squirrel gathers leaves
high in a tree.
He makes his nest warm
for the cold winter weather.

nest

But a nest in the treetops
is too high for a dormouse.
The dormouse looks up,
then scurries by.

A queen wasp sleeps
under an oak stump.
She has squeezed through
a crack in the rotten wood.

stump

But a crack in an oak stump
is too small for a dormouse.
The dormouse looks in,
then scurries by.

A golden-eyed toad sleeps
under a stone.
It is muddy and wet and
the toad's skin is cold.

But it's too wet for a dormouse
under a stone.
The dormouse looks in,
then scurries by.

A mother brown bear
sleeps in a den.
She is furry and warm.
She stretches and yawns.

den

The dormouse looks in.
The bear's teeth are huge!
The dormouse trembles …
then scurries by.

cave

Bats hang in a cave and
cling to the rock.
They huddle together and
sleep through the winter.

The cave is damp and dark.
It's too cold for a dormouse.
The dormouse looks in,
then scurries by.

A family of rabbits
hop into their burrow.
They live underground
when the weather is cold.
But there are too many rabbits
to make room for a dormouse.

burrow

The dormouse
looks in,
then scurries by.

An owl
with sharp claws
flies over the meadow.
He is hungry
and watchful.
He is hunting
for mice.

The owl swoops!
The dormouse
hides in a bush.

Where can she find
a safe bed
for the winter?

A deer comes to the meadow.
She nibbles the grass.
Her coat has grown thick
for the cold winter weather.

The dormouse shivers in the wind,
then scurries by.

A storm is coming.
The sky has turned black.

Bees fly home
to their hive.

hive

Ants run to their nest.

The dormouse waits
under a branch
for the storm to pass by.
Where can she find
a safe bed for the winter?

A snake slides through the grass.

He has hungry black eyes.

He stares at the dormouse.

His tongue flicks in and out.

The dormouse
is trapped.
She's too scared
to move.

The snake slithers closer.
His forked tongue comes nearer.

BOOM!
Thunder rumbles.
CRACK!
Lightning flashes.

The snake stops for a second,
then shoots into the grass.

The dormouse runs
through the meadow.
Her heart pounds like a drum.
She climbs up a tree trunk.

tree trunk

She crawls into a hole.
She finds a place
that is safe and dry!

Snow falls on the meadow.
The ground is
frozen and hard.
Snug in the tree hole,
the dormouse is sleeping.
Her long, fluffy tail
is wrapped tightly
round her.

Her search is over.
The dormouse is safe.
At last she has found
her bed for the winter!

Picture Word List

meadow

cave

nest

burrow

stump

hive

den

tree trunk

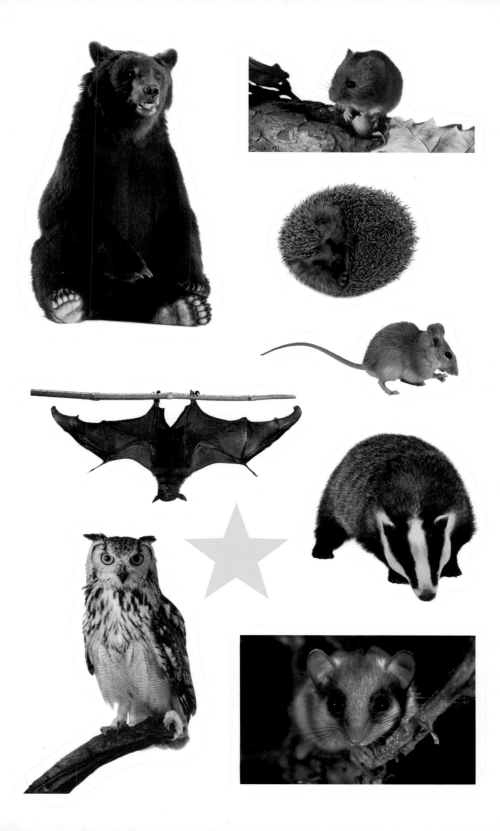

Sainsbury's
Reading Scheme

CERTIFICATE
of READING

My name is

_____

I have read

_____

Date

_____